Reinhold Moritzevič Glière

Two Pieces
Zwei Stücke

for Double Bass and Piano · für Kontrabass und Klavier

op. 9

F 95084

ROB. FORBERG MUSIKVERLAG

INDEX · INHALT

ISMN 979-0-2061-0618-7

1. Intermezzo 3

2. Tarantella 7

Cover image · Umschlagbild: M. Čiurlionis, *Sonata della Stella. Allegro* (1908)

F 95084
ISMN 979-0-2061-0618-7

À Monsieur S. Koussevitzky

Two Pieces · Zwei Stücke
Intermezzo

Reinhold Moritzevič Glière
op. 9/1

Kontrabass

Klavier

© 2019 by Rob. Forberg Musikverlag, Berlin

F 95084

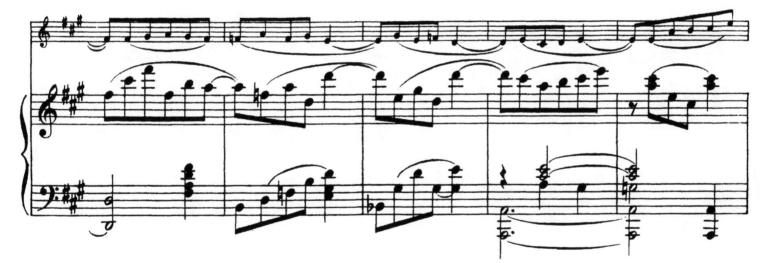

Tarantella

op. 9/2

Meno mosso.

Meno mosso.

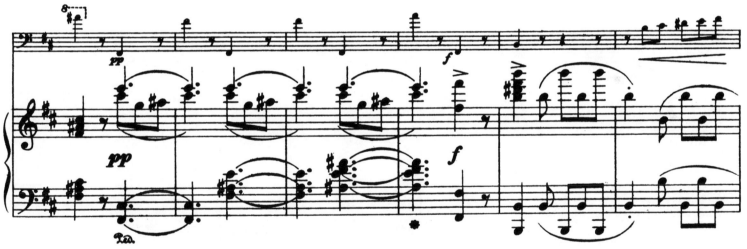

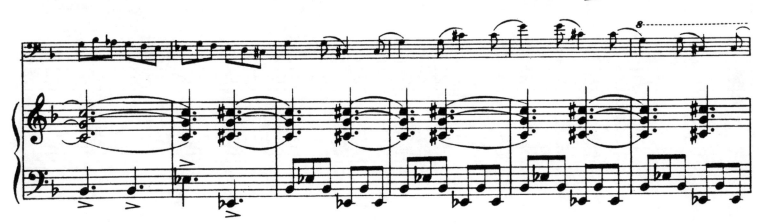

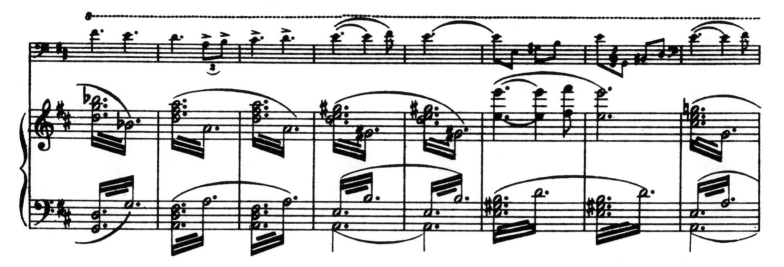